The Brockbank Omnibus

Other books by Russell Brockbank

★

Round the Bend
Up the Straight
Over the Line
Published by Temple Press Ltd.

★

(*with Ronald Collier*)
Bees Under my Bonnet

★

(*with Rodney Walkerley*)
Motoring Abroad
More Motoring Abroad

RUSSELL BROCKBANK

The Brockbank Omnibus

G. P. PUTNAM'S SONS   NEW YORK

acknowledgement

Grateful acknowledgement is made to
the Proprietors of PUNCH for per-
mission to reproduce the drawings
in this book, all of which originally
appeared in their pages.

R.B.

For
Eileen
Roger & Susan
who saw all these coming

—Brockbank

"Golly, they've been a long time selling that one!"

MONTE CARLO MANIA

"Flyovers, Motorways, and such! What's the matter with the roads we've got?"

"You mis-guided missile, you!"

"My *driving examiner* would fail the lot."

"Straight on be quicker, but t'other be prettier."

"*I've checked the Dynasurge Drive, the Gas Miser and the Hydromatic Sweetsurger, and I'm still short of Fireball Power.*"

"*I should have thought there was enough crime in the newspapers without having it in real life, too.*"

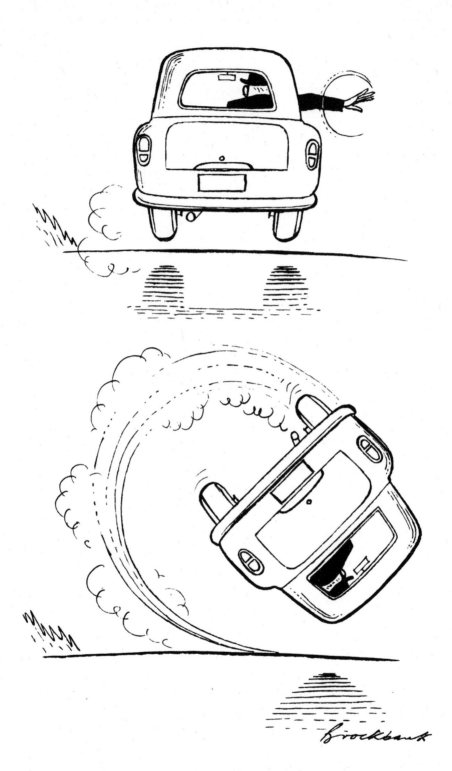

The day petrol rationing ended

"Time of arrival 14 hours, 37 minutes, 7 secs. . . .

. . . 8 secs. . . . . .9 secs. . . .''

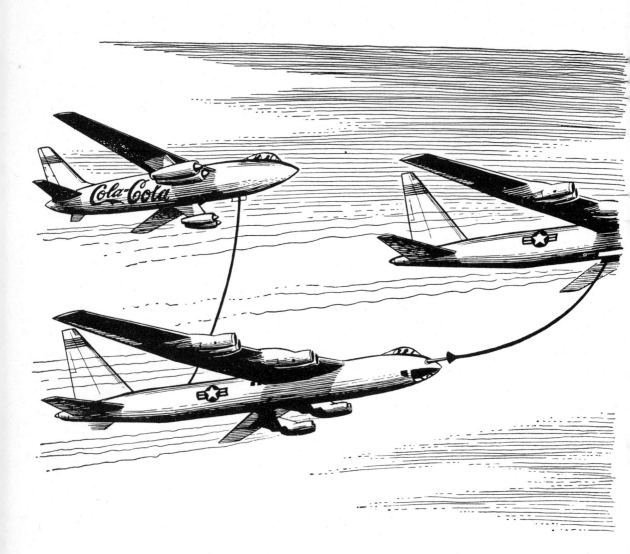

" . . . and there is a gentleman from the Dingbat Aero Company waiting outside."

"I assure Madam she is facing the engine."

"But they are switched off — look!"

*"What a superb example of man's conquest of the air is
the modern military aircraft—*

—especially when landing.

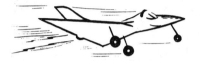

*Here he comes—
Wheels down—*

—flaps down—

—touch down—

—braking parachute out—

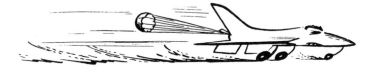

—brakes on—

—brakes on—I see he's let out another 'chute—

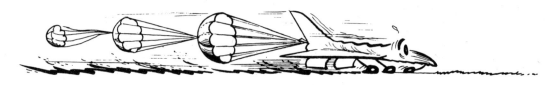

—and another—

—whew!''

Brockbank

"*Just another Reserve Officer stepping out on to a wing that isn't there any more.*"

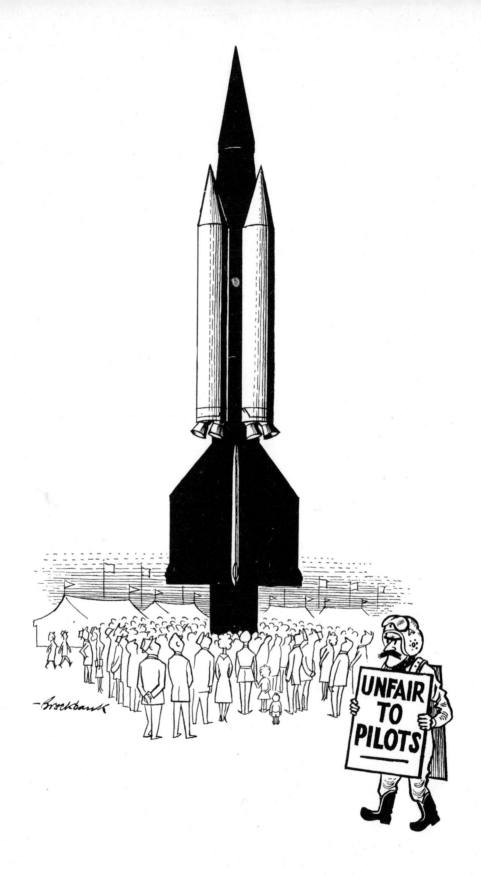

"I said we're travelling faster than sound, now!"

"Did you by any chance go through the sound barrier at 4:37 P.M. today?"

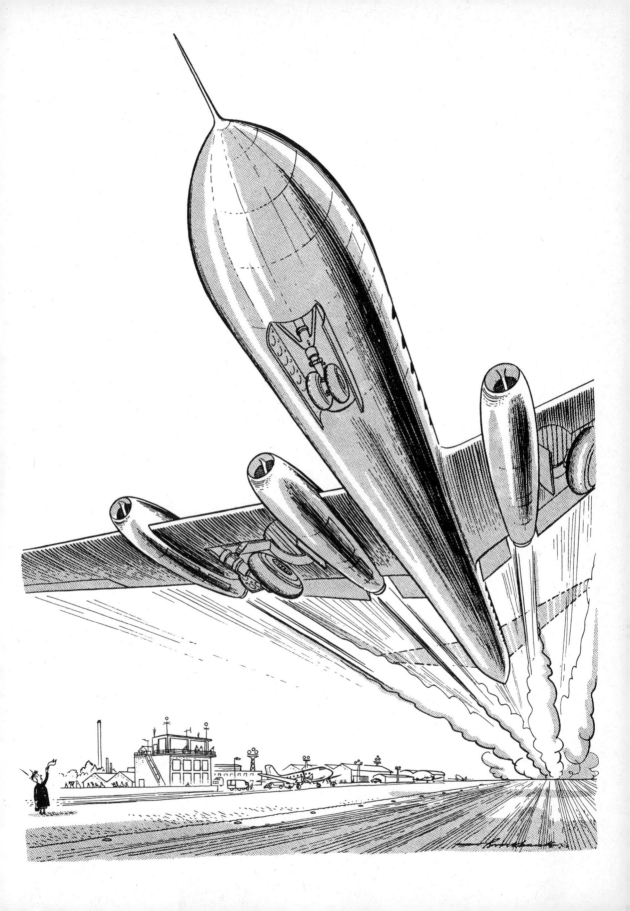

"Anyway, we don't have to stand them drinks in the mess."

"They're accurate to a thou., so there's no need to keep saying 'And the best of luck.'"

*"They're only breaking these blasted records so they can do us
out of complimentary meals."*

"We liked it here so much we haven't bothered to go any further."

First day of the 'No Hooting' rule in Paris

"Why, Mr. Moskvitch, I thought we said goodbye at the Polish frontier."

Brockbank

"So that's Son et Lumière!"

"*While you're about it, ask him if he knows a good place for lunch.*"

"On your way past, would you mind asking my husband not to drive so fast?"

*"You know perfectly well the insurance certificate is in the top left-hand
drawer of the desk your Auntie Frances left us."*

"*Disappointing, rather.*"

"*Get a load of the air hostess.*"

"*Nobody bothered to inform me about any change over to larger aircraft.*"

"That's nothing like the 'Turning Left' signal you taught me."

"Mind that rut . . . you're too high . . . look out for the blind corner . . . we'll never make it . . ."

Brockbank

"In 2 m. t. rt. (A9932) and in ¼ m. t. lt. (unclass). Cross R. br. and t. rt., 5/3 m. farther t. rt. uphill. In 2 m. over X-rds. then t. lt., 3/4 m. farther t. rt. into narrow lane to Easthill. Do not miss ancient white cross on lt. . . ."

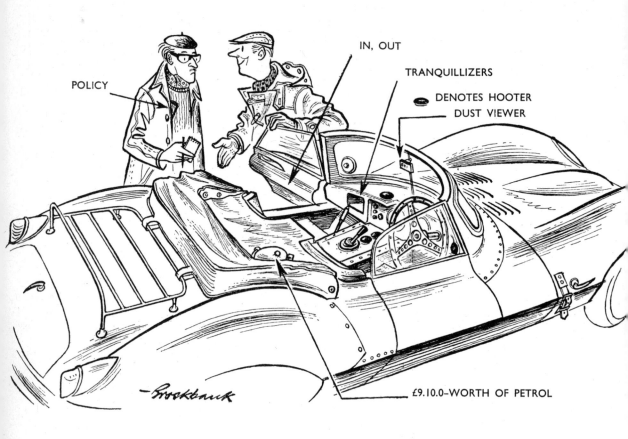

POLICY

IN, OUT

TRANQUILLIZERS

● DENOTES HOOTER
DUST VIEWER

—Brockbank

£9.10.0-WORTH OF PETROL

Jaguar XK "SS"

Weight ....17½ cwt.
250 b.h.p. at 6000 r.p.m.
Max. top speed ....160 m.p.h.
Accel. 0–60, 4.7 secs., 0–80, 8 secs., 0–100, 12.1 sec.
Max. gear speeds, 1st 67, 2nd 78, 3rd 112, top 160.

Speedier cars may be the answer to over-crowded highways. The faster the car, the sooner it vacates road space for others. With this in mind, RUSSELL BROCKBANK and J. B. BOOTHROYD recently took out a Jaguar XK "SS" and a flattering amount of short-term life insurance.

RESIDENTS on the test route will not need telling that we followed the line Guildford-Winchester-Salisbury. They will remember us.

There is only one of these motor-cars in the country, the rest having run off the edge, got stuck under milk tankers, or gone to America, where longer, wider and straighter roads, with fewer tractors towing hay-wains in the middle of them, enable short bursts of maximum speed to be achieved until such time as the police can organize road-blocks ahead by short-wave. As no more are to be made we had the additional satisfaction of knowing that we were testing the fastest museum-piece in existence. The passenger, in particular, found such additional satisfaction welcome. He could do with some. His accommodation was grudging and limited, gouged out of the surrounding mass like a small hole in stiff, hot porridge (the exhaust system travels up his left leg before clotting on the car's nearside exterior). His share of the fascia cuts him sharply below the kneecaps, or, later, when cringing sets in with the legs well drawn up, across the shinbone. The hand-brake will be found to fit conveniently up his right sleeve. The driver, if his boots aren't too wide, finds no difficulty in depressing the control pedals independently of each other, and can comfortably extend his legs to a squatting position. Over 100 m.p.h. he feels the cold, and wonders if there is any quick way of transferring half a dozen hot pipes to his side of the car.

There are four hooter buttons, two of which are sited near the gearshift and tend to be sounded simultaneously with the change — just when, in fact, warning of approach is not needed. It was found wise in our case, when the passenger often wanted to hoot as well, to come to an agreement on whose fingers should fly to which button. This worked well, particularly as the driver tended to use the one in the centre of the wheel, which, as it happened, wasn't one.

There is no luggage accommodation. Space which might otherwise be handy for trunks, folding perambulators, playpens, sacks of lawn sand and the like is given over to thirty-eight gallons of fuel. The model tested was in Post Office red, with damp handprints on the passenger's door.

It was a fine autumn morning with a crispness in the air when, with dry roads and lips, we took off in a south-westerly direction. We at once entered Hampshire, twelve miles distant, at 96 m.p.h., and changed into top. By this time the portion of the passenger projecting above the windshield had the sensation of being embedded in an ice-block, though his socks, by way of compensation, were already hot to the touch.

The car was not offensively noisy, so far as it was possible to judge. That is, no adverse criticism was actually heard from scattering road-gangs, rocking wayside coffee-stalls or a middle-aged couple near Liphook whose picnic was blown up a grass bank. The noise is less a car noise than a pleasing *musique concrète* of wounded bison (engine), nose-flutes in ecstasy (tyres), and pigs at slaughter (disc brakes); in slow running the orchestration is further added to by spittings on giant flat-irons to simulate the six dyspeptic carburetters. This last effect, however, came in only after a rigid throttling down to 70-75 m.p.h. to conform to the requirements of built-up area restrictions.

A notable aspect of the test was the good behavior of other motorists noticeable throughout. Even drivers clearly unaccustomed to being overtaken put their nearside wheels on the verge and waved us on just after we had gone past.

Lunch was taken in Salisbury, where some delay was experienced while the passenger, now shaped like an old soup-tin pressed for remelting, was prised out by the half-dozen heavy, fresh-faced young men in one-piece caps and fur-collared duffle coats who had been drawn from nearby driving-wheels and wished to see, stroke, sniff and otherwise investigate the car. One of these insisted on joining us in the dining-room of the Cathedral Hotel, but would neither take anything nor remove his outer clothing in case we drove away suddenly and robbed him of the spectacle. We tried to turn his conversation from single dry plate clutches and protected air intakes by asking whether our chosen parking-site was police-proof, but he dismissed this as meaningless delirium and plunged into some exhaust manifolding on a DB3S Aston Martin. He later indulged us by saying that Salisbury was a very pro-motoring city, and never prosecuted cars of over 200 b.h.p.

On re-entering the car and beginning the return journey it was found that the passenger's lunch was folded up under the breastbone, where it promised to be a lasting obstruction. This proved to have been distributed more equably over the digestive system shortly after Alresford, where a smart piece of braking from 120 m.p.h. to a near standstill (58 m.p.h.), as a tribute to three motor-coaches overtaking two more round a bend, arrested an interesting zoom-lens effect and turned the driver's cap through 360 degrees.

To sum up, the "SS" isn't everyone's

car. Everyone couldn't get in it. It eats up an immense amount of road, converting a ten-mile stretch of straight into something the size of a bus-ticket — and thus detracting from the finer points of the scenery. But for the man who wants to leave as much road **as** empty as possible for other people, who likes to overtake a convoy of six sand-and-gravel lorries with trailers in a space which the ordinary motorist would regard as a tight squeeze for overtaking an elderly lady pushing a bicycle, who doesn't mind having his passenger's boots on fire and a wife who sits by the telephone with palpitations as soon as the sound of his exhaust has died away, it may be said to exhibit certain points of advantage.

"I see the leaves are on the turn."

"*I name this ship Veuve Cliquot 1937 . . .*"

"Want to know the cricket results?"

"My father's a racing driver."

"I'd like to see those blasted satellites do five miles a second under these conditions."

"I knew there would be a snag to this Press-button Warfare."

"*Ah, shut up!*"

"No doubt Pakistan is grateful for lend lease."

"I've been called up."

BRANCH ISSUE